RUDYARD KIPLING'S

HOW THE ELEPHANT GOT HIS TRUNK

THE GRAPHIC NOVEL

Hoena & Rodriguez

RUDYARD KIPLING

EST. 1865

TO OUR READERS

The animal world has long been a place of intrigue. Countless mysteries surround its magnificent creatures. For years, humankind has wondered how animals came to look and act the way they do.

Finally, the questions have been answered. Famed author and worldwide explorer Rudyard Kipling has traveled the globe, searching for the greatest of beasts. He's witnessed and recorded animal behaviors unlike anything seen before. And now he is sharing his findings with the world.

Let Kipling be your guide as you journey into jungles, grasslands, and deserts. Use his invaluable research to unravel the mysteries yourself. It is an exciting time for animal lovers. Thanks to Kipling, we can all be part of it.

Sincerely,
The Editors

HOW THE ELEPHANT GOT HIS TRUNK

RESEARCH

SPECIMEN:
BOOT-NOSED ELEPHANT
(Fig. A)

HABITAT: Africa, near the Limpopo River (Fig. C)
SOCIAL BEHAVIOR: Insatiably curious
PARENTAL UNIT: Mother elephant (Fig. B)
ADVISOR: Mr. Snake (Fig. D)
ELDERS: Hippopotomus (Fig. E), Giraffe (Fig. F), Baboon (Fig. G), Aunty Ozzy (Fig. H)
PREDATOR: Crocodile (Fig. I)

Short, stubby nose

Insatiable curiosity

A

B

NAMIBIA

BOTSWANA

MOZAMBIQUE

SOUTH AFRICA

C

D

E

F

G

H

I

Long ago, in a far-off time, elephants had no trunks. Rather, they had big, bulgy noses shaped somewhat like boots.

All they could do with these odd noses was wiggle them from side to side.

WIGGLE
WIGGLE

. . . the Elephant Child, who had an insatiable curiosity. That is, he asked a lot of questions.

Ely, leave Mr. Dung Beetle *alone.*

Now *hurry up* and join the herd, or you'll be left *behind.*

Coming, Mother!

Mom?

Yes, dear?

Why is the sky *blue?*

Well, I —

Often, his curiosity got him into trouble.

Aunty Ozzy!

Yes, Ely?

Why's your bottom covered in feathers?

Mine's not.

Well, I . . .

As he walked away, the Elephant Child came across the Kolokolo Bird.

Why so *glum,* Ely, my chum?

This is why!

Oh my, your rump is as *red* as Baboon's *butt!*

All of the animals have *spanked me* because of my insatiable curiosity. But there is *one thing* I just need to know.

What is *that,* my *curious* elephant?

As the Elephant Child traveled, there was one thing he realized he hadn't thought of.

He had never seen a crocodile before.

Excuse me, *Mr. Snake.* But have you ever *seen* a *crocodile?*

Why yes, *I have.*

Then do you *know* where I can *find* one?

The banks of the great *Limpopo River* are just over the next hill. *There* you'll find a *crocodile.*

Thank you, Mr. Snake.

I'd better follow that young elephant, or he may get himself in *terrible trouble.*

So Ely sat back on his haunches and pulled and pulled . . .

. . . and the Crocodile thrashed in the water and pulled and pulled . . .

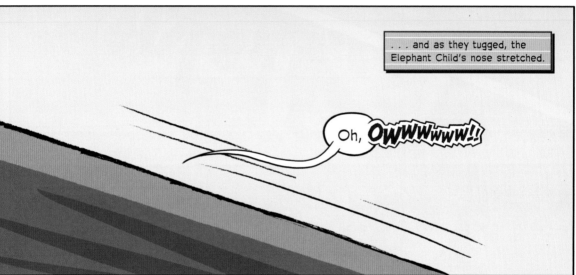

. . . and as they tugged, the Elephant Child's nose stretched.

Oh, **OWWWwww!!**

Ow, *owwww,* this is *too buch* for *be!*

Something had changed for the Elephant Child.

There's an *advantage* to having a long nose — *swatting flies!*

I suppose. And *I suppose* it's time to *head home* now.

After a long while . . .

I'm getting *hungry.*

Why don't you *reach up* and *grab* one of those fruits?

YOINK

And there's *another* advantage to your new nose — *grabbing food.*

And once the other elephants saw the Elephant Child's new trunk, they went to visit the Crocodile to get their own.

I keep six honest serving-men:
        (They taught me all I knew)
Their names are What and Where and When
        And How and Why and Who.
I send them over land and sea,
        I send them east and west;
But after they have worked for me,
        I give them all a rest.

I let them rest from nine till five.
        For I am busy then,
As well as breakfast, lunch, and tea,
        For they are hungry men:
But different folk have different views:
        I know a person small—
She keeps ten million serving-men,
        Who get no rest at all!

She sends 'em abroad on her own affairs,
        From the second she opens her eyes—
One million Hows, two million Wheres,
        And seven million Whys! *

* Poem by Rudyard Kipling.

33

CONCLUSION

NEW SPECIMEN:
LONG-TRUNKED ELEPHANT

84 An adult African elephant's trunk is about seven feet long. Even though noses are very long, nose jobs are unheard of in elephant social circles.

If threatened, an elephant uses its trunk to make loud trumpeting noises. Would love to hear a jazz combo built around this incredible sound.

Elephants sometimes hug each other with their trunks. Must be a hugger to run with this group.

zZz An elephant sleeps an average of just two hours during a 24-hour period. No wonder the young elephant's mother was so cranky.

84

1

2

3

4

5

LEARN MORE

Use this handy list of terms and questions to get you started on your own research of the magnificent elephant!

TERMS

advantage	(ad-VAN-tij)—something that helps or is useful
curiosity	(kyur-ee-AHSS-i-tee)—an eagerness to learn things or find things out
haunches	(HAWNCH-es)—the hips, buttocks, and upper thighs of an animal or person
immediately	(i-MEE-dee-it-lee)—now or at once
insatiable	(in-SAY-shuh-buhl)—impossible to satisfy
instantly	(IN-stuhnt-lee)—happening right away
Limpopo River	(lim-POH-poh RIV-er)—a river in South Africa

DISCUSSION

1. Why did Ely's questions upset the adults?

2. Why do you think the snake was willing to help the elephant child?

3. Kipling ended his "research" on the elephant with a poem. Discuss the meaning behind the poem.

RESEARCH

1. Kipling wrote how the elephant got his trunk. Write your own story about how he got his large, flappy ears.

2. What would you do with a trunk? Write a paragraph on it.

3. When the other elephants saw Ely's trunk, they decided to visit the crocodile to get their own. Record what happens when one of them goes by drawing and writing a series of panels about it.

Rudyard Kipling

RUDYARD KIPLING
Founder/Guide

Joseph Rudyard Kipling was born in Bombay, India, on December 30, 1865. He is best known for his short story collections *The Jungle Book*, published in 1894, and *Just So Stories*, published in 1902. He wrote a variety of other short stories, including "Kim" and "The Man Who Would Be King," and many poems. In 1907, he received the Nobel Prize in Literature, becoming the first English-language writer and youngest person to win the award. On January 18, 1936, he died in London at age 70.

BLAKE A. HOENA
Retelling author

Blake A. Hoena grew up in Wisconsin. In his youth, he wrote stories about robots conquering the Moon and trolls lumbering around in the woods behind his house. Blake has written more than forty books for children, including graphic novel retellings of "The Legend of Sleepy Hollow", "Jack and the Beanstalk", and the Perseus and Medusa myth.

PEDRO RODRIGUEZ
Illustrator

Pedro Rodriguez studied illustration at the Fine Arts School in Barcelona, Spain. He has worked in design, marketing, and advertising, creating books, logos, animated films, and music videos. Rodriguez lives in Barcelona with his wife, Gemma, and their daughter, Maya.

JULIE GASSMAN	editor
DONALD LEMKE	managing editor
MICHAEL DAHL	editorial director
BOB LENTZ	designer & letterer
HEATHER KINDSETH	creative director

1

2

3

4

5

ALSO AVAILABLE FROM ...

RUDYARD
KIPLING

EST.
1865

Published by Capstone Global Library Limited, a company incorporated in England and Wales having its registered office at 7 Pilgrim Street, London, EC4V 6LB - Registered company number: 6695582

Text © Raintree 2012   First published in India in 2012
The moral rights of the proprietor have been asserted.

ISBN 978-1-406-25360-3 (paperback)
16 15 14 13 12
10 9 8 7 6 5 4 3 2 1

A full catalogue record for this book is available from the British Library

Printed at Multivista Global Limited

www.raintreepublishers.co.uk
Email: myorders@raintreepublishers.co.uk

Bloomington, Chicago, Mankato, Oxford